by Norma Simon

Illustrations by Harvey Weiss

United Synagogue Commission on Jewish Education

שַׁבָּת

Every Friday Night

Copyright © 1961 by United Synagogue of America—Printed in U.S.A.

Shabbat begins every Friday night.
The sun goes down behind all the houses.

My father is home from a week of work,
and we are all together.

The white tablecloth covers our table. The *Ḥallot* are covered and just the ends are showing.

My mother lights the candles.
My mother covers her eyes.
My mother says the *B'rakhah*.
*Ba-rukh a-tah Ado-nai, Elo-he-nu me-lekh
 ha-olam, a-sher kid-sha-nu b'mitz-vo-tav,
 v'tzi-va-nu l'had-lik ner shel Shab-bat.*
David and I say, "Amen."

The silver *Kiddush* cup is full of wine.
My father holds the cup high.
My father says the *Kiddush*,
    the *B'rakhah* for wine.
Ba-rukh a-tah Ado-nai, Elo-he-nu me-lekh
    ha-olam, bo-rey p'ri ha-ga-fen.
Mother, David and I say, "Amen,"
    and then we all taste the wine.

        This is how *Shabbat* begins.

Father says:

Ba-rukh a-tah Ado-nai, Elo-he-nu me-lekh ha-olam, ha-motzi le-ḥem min ha-a-retz.

And we all eat
a piece of *Ḥallah*.

I like to have a holiday every week
　　with the house so clean,
　　with my clothes so pretty,
　　with my whole family
　　sitting all around our table.

I like my mother's cooking
especially for *Shabbat*.
David likes *gefilte fish* with a carrot on top.

Daddy likes the *Ḥallot,*   our special bread
for *Shabbat*.

I like the chicken full of soft stuffing,
full of chewy bones,

We all wait for *Shabbat* every Friday night.

Holidays are once a year.
Once they are over,　　it's a long, long time
until they come again.

But every Friday night,
> when school is over for David and for me;
> every Friday night,
> when Daddy's work is done,
> *Shabbat* comes again.

After dinner, we hear a knock on the door.
Grandma and Grandpa are here
 for a *Shabbat* visit.
"*Shabbat Shalom!*" "*Shabbat Shalom!*"
 everyone shouts.
Grandma and Grandpa kiss David and me.

David has so much to tell to
 Grandma and Grandpa,
 he wants to talk first.
I have so much to tell to
 Grandma and Grandpa,
 I want to talk first.

We both talk at once.
Everybody laughs
    and then we each take turns.
Grandma listens   and Grandpa listens
    until the doorbell rings.

Dorothy, our sitter, is at the door.
David and I run to see her.
Dorothy comes every Friday night,
    when Mother and Daddy
        go to synagogue.

Mother,
　　Daddy,
　　　　Grandma,
　　　　　and Grandpa
　　　　　　go to synagogue
　　　　　　　every Friday night.
"Good night, children.　Good night, Dorothy."
　　David,
　　　　Dorothy,
　　　　　and I
　　　　　　stand
　　　　　　　and
　　　　　　　　wave
　　　　　　　　　good-bye.

When Mother and Daddy come home from synagogue, David is fast asleep.

Mother and I walk to the door with Dorothy, our sitter.

"Good-bye, Dorothy," we say.

"Good-bye," Dorothy says, "I'll see you all next Friday night."

Grandma and Grandpa come back to our house.
Sometimes friends come to talk and sing.

I stay up a little later on *Shabbat* night.
I sleep a little later on *Shabbat* morning.
I feel very sleepy.
I say, *"Shabbat Shalom!"* to everyone.

Mother tucks me into bed.
She gives me a quiet kiss.
She whispers a soft *"Shabbat Shalom!"*
I whisper *"Shabbat Shalom"* to her.

WORDS FOR PRONUNCIATION AND DEFINITION

B'rakhah (B'rah-KHAH)   A blessing or a prayer.

Hallot (Hal-LOT)   White loaves of Sabbath bread.

Kiddush (Kid-DOOSH)   Prayer recited over a cup of wine.

Shabbat (Shab-BAT)   Sabbath.

Shalom (Shah-LOME)   (Peace) Hello or Good-bye.